The pivot is the human scale: the sleeping man at the picnic, captured in a view 1 meter square from 1 meter away. Our point of view is always perpendicular to this man. Therefore, every image on every page, out to the outermost power, is centered on the nucleus of an atom in the hand of the sleeping man. Following that path, this flipbook offers a journey of 38 powers of ten. It takes 2 pages per power. That means that starting at the front (big going towards small), every 2 pages you see a view ten times smaller than the view 2 pages earlier. Or if you are starting at the back (small going towards big), every two pages you see a view ten times larger than the view 2 pages earlier. Since every image is centered on the same point, any given page is a detail from the center of the next higher page and has the next lower page nested within it. [The intermediate pages represent the view from a point approximately half way between each level of magnitude.]

Starting at the picnic, after 23 powers of ten, each time leaping 10 times further, we would find ourselves at 10^{-23} meters, 10 million light years out, roughly 3 orders of magnitude from the edge of the observable universe. And, by diving in 15 powers of ten from the picnic, each time cutting our field of view down to a tenth of its previous size, we would arrive at 10^{-15} meters, the scale of a proton, or about 3 orders of magnitude from the scale of a quark. As you can confirm by counting the powers for yourself, if that tiny proton were one unit, then the biggest square (ten million light years) would be 10^{-38}, or 100,000,000,000,000,000,000,000,000,000,000,000,000 of those units.

The images in this flipbook come from the film Powers of Ten by Charles and Ray Eames, the husband and wife team ranked among the most important designers of the 20th Century. Best known for their furniture, they also made landmark contributions to architecture, graphics, and communications. One of their more than 100 short films, Powers of Ten expresses a key part of their design approach: the value of looking at things from the next largest frame of reference, and the next smallest. • Powers of Ten is also available on video, as an informative book, and, most recently, as a CD-ROM of 6 parallel adventures in scale. Contact the Eames Office for more information.
• This flipbook is a co-production of Optical Toys and the Eames Office.

~10 million light years

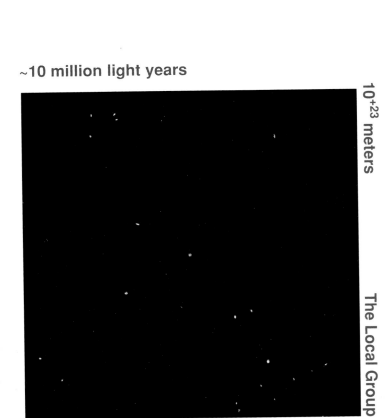

10⁺²³ meters

The Local Group

~1 million light years

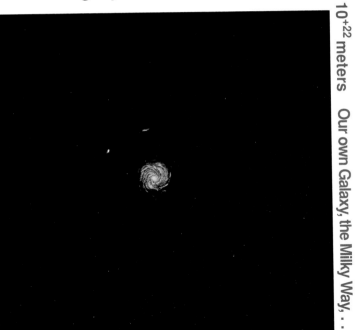

10^{+22} meters   Our own Galaxy, the Milky Way, . . .

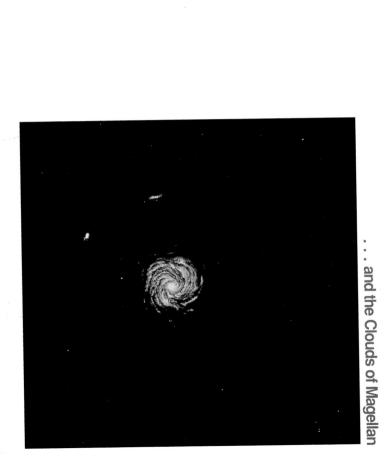

. . . and the Clouds of Magellan

~100,000 light years

10^{+21} meters

The Milky Way

~10,000 light years

10^{+20} meters Clouds of stars and glowing gas . . .

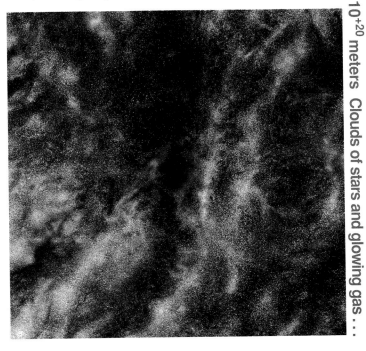

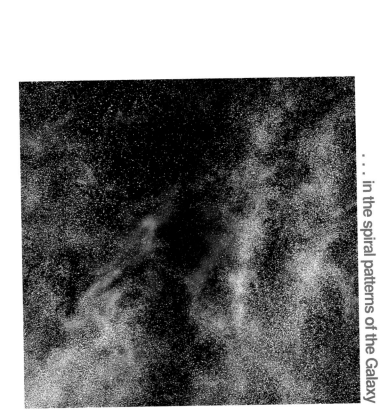

. . . in the spiral patterns of the Galaxy

~1,000 light years

10+19 meters   Stars in the disc of the Milky Way

~100 light years

10^{+18} meters

That red star is Arcturus

~10 light years

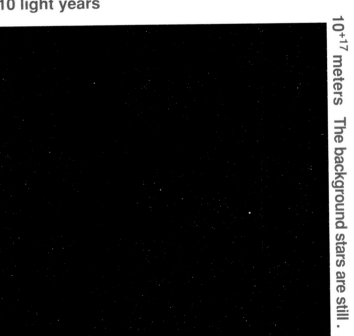

10^{+17} meters The background stars are still . . .

. . . so far away they appear . . .

~1 light year

10^{+16} meters . . . unchanged for several powers;

the dot in the center . . .

1 trillion kilometers

10⁺¹⁵ meters

. . . is the distant Sun.

100 billion kilometers

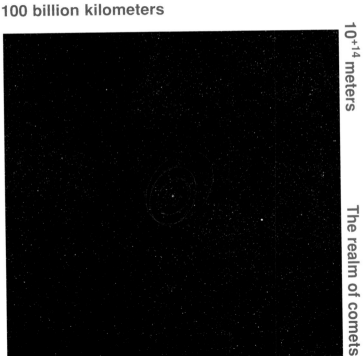

10⁺¹⁴ meters

The realm of comets

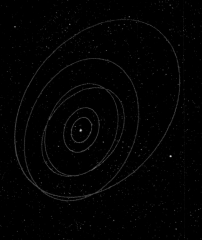

10 billion kilometers

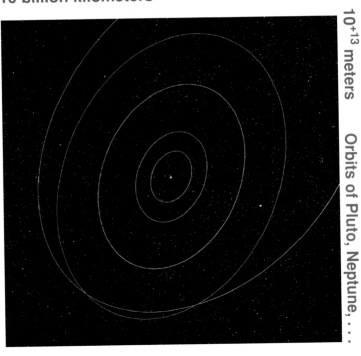

10⁺¹³ meters   Orbits of Pluto, Neptune, . . .

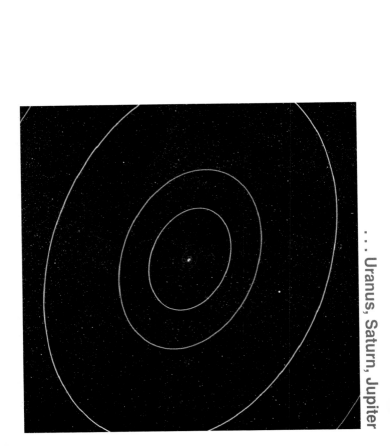

. . . Uranus, Saturn, Jupiter

1 billion kilometers

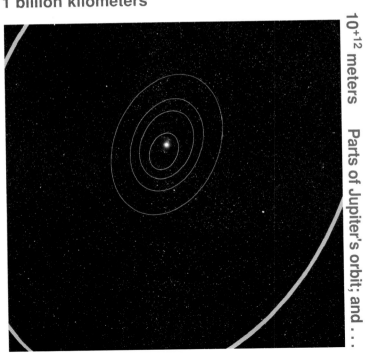

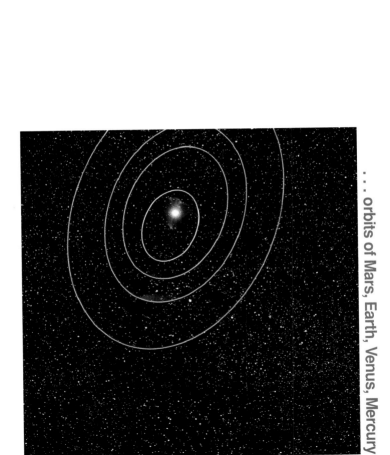

... orbits of Mars, Earth, Venus, Mercury

100 million kilometers

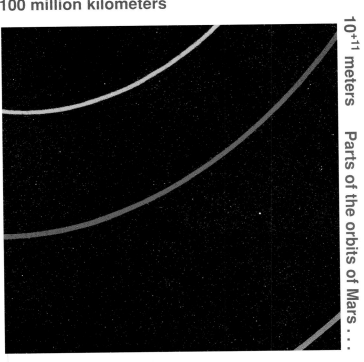

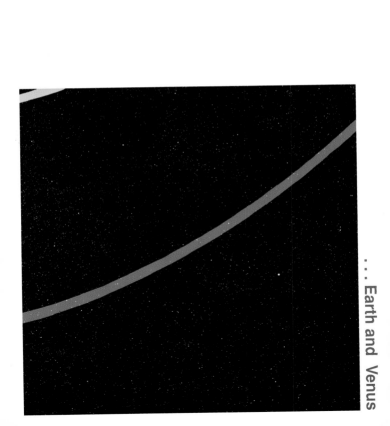

. . . Earth and Venus

10 million kilometers

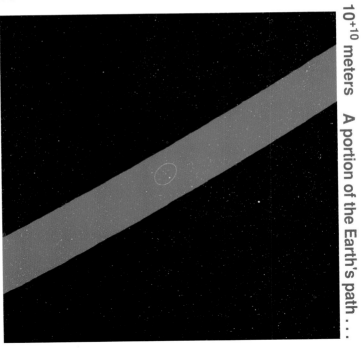

10^{+10} meters   A portion of the Earth's path . . .

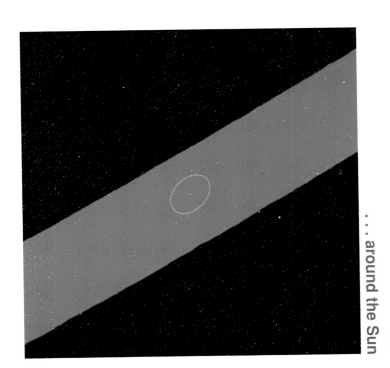

. . . around the Sun

1 million kilometers

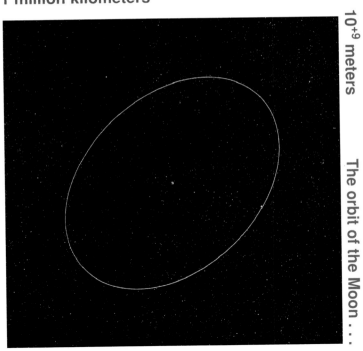

10^{+9} meters

The orbit of the Moon . . .

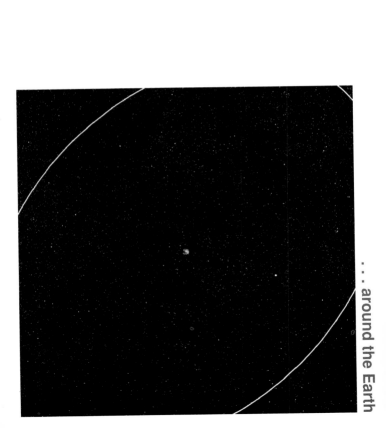

. . . around the Earth

100,000 kilometers

10+8 meters The Earth against background stars

10,000 kilometers

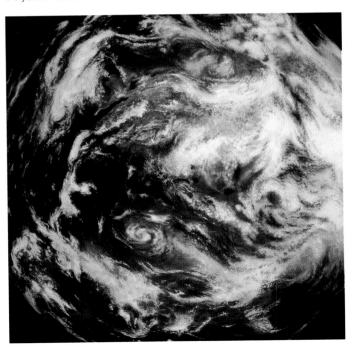

10^{+7} meters

The Earth

1,000 kilometers

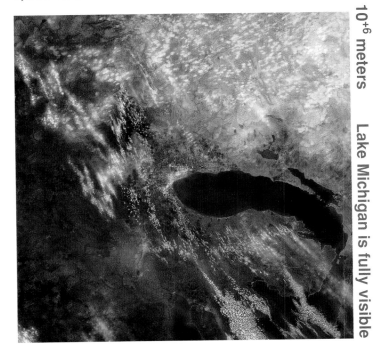

10⁺⁶ meters

Lake Michigan is fully visible

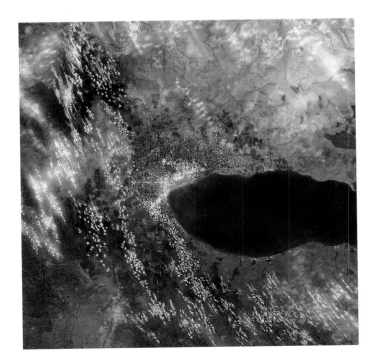

100 kilometers

10+5 meters

The greater Chicago area

10 kilometers

10^{+4} meters

Chicago by the lake shore

1 kilometer

10+3 meters

Soldier Field and . . .

. . . Lake Shore Drive

10 meters

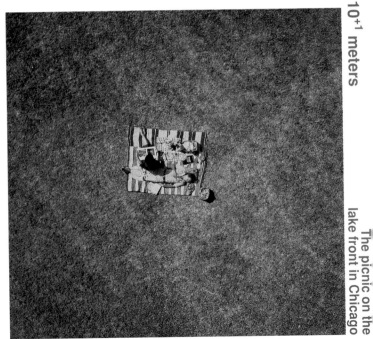

The picnic on the
lake front in Chicago

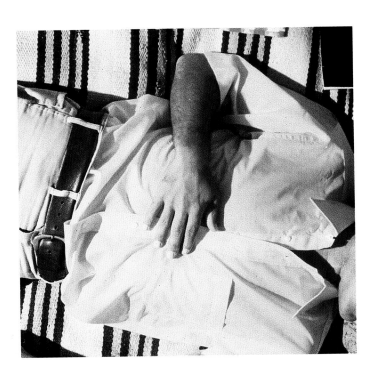

10 centimeters

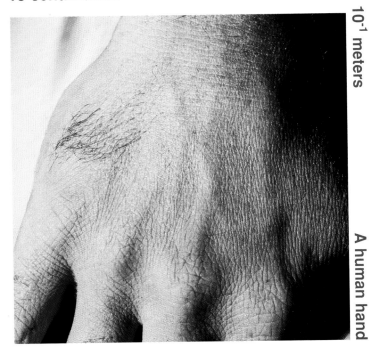

10⁻¹ meters

A human hand

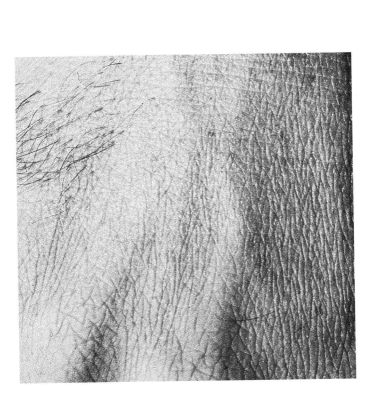

1 centimeter

10⁻² meters

The skin

1 millimeter

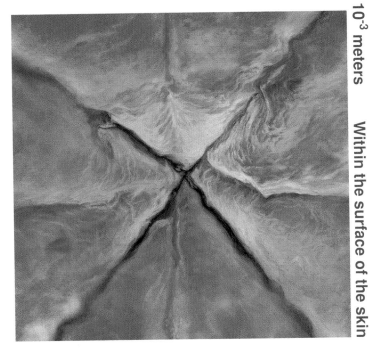

10⁻³ meters

Within the surface of the skin

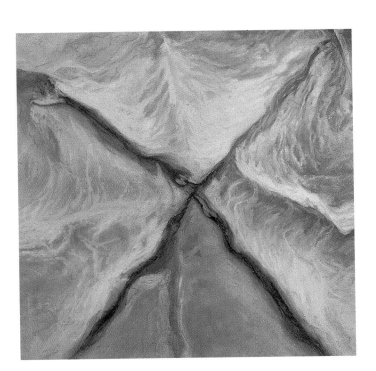

100 microns

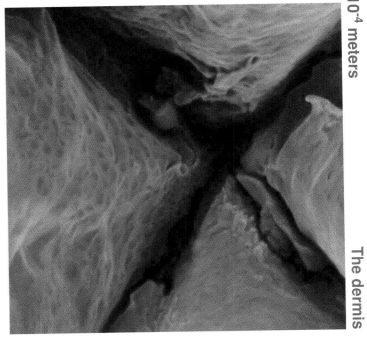

10⁻⁴ meters

The dermis

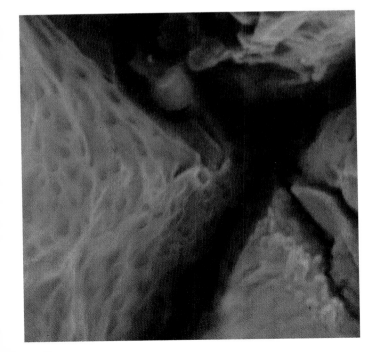

Explaining the
Transition: the
ruffly lympho-
cyte seen at
10^{-5} is located
in a capillary
just beneath
the surface of
the hand.

10 microns

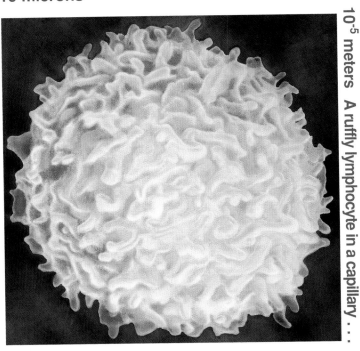

10^{-5} meters   A ruffly lymphocyte in a capillary . . .

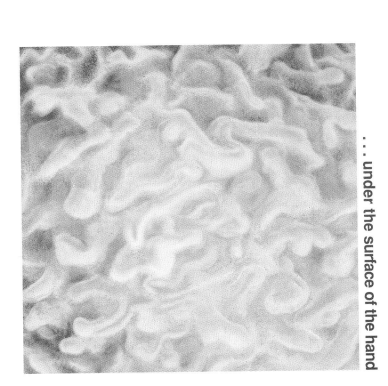

. . . under the surface of the hand

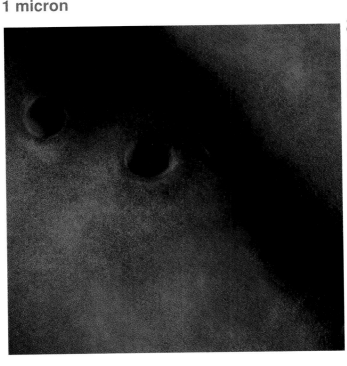

1 micron

Explaining the Transition: the dark surface seen at 10^{-6} is not a detail of the surface of the ruffly lymphocyte, but rather a detail of the nucleus of that cell.

10^{-6} meters   The wall of that cell's nucleus

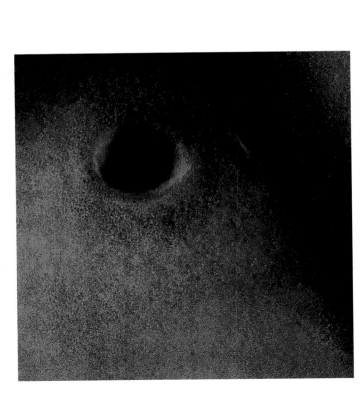

Explaining the Transition: the DNA you see at 10^{-7} is contained within the nucleus whose surface you see at the next larger image.

1,000 angstroms (100 nanometers)

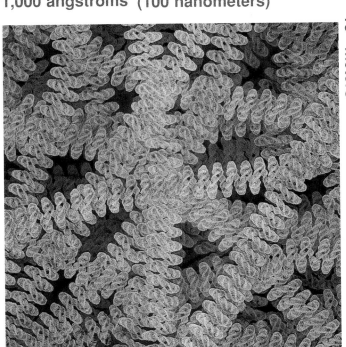

10^{-7} meters

DNA

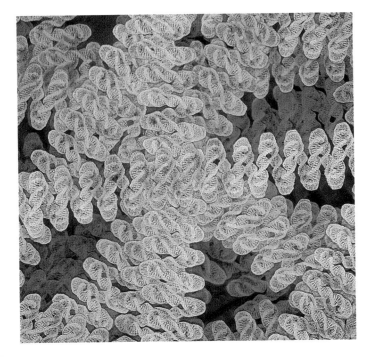

100 angstroms (10 nanometers)

10^{-8} meters

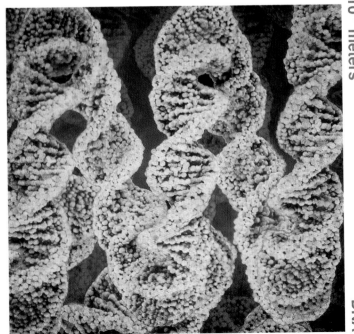

DNA

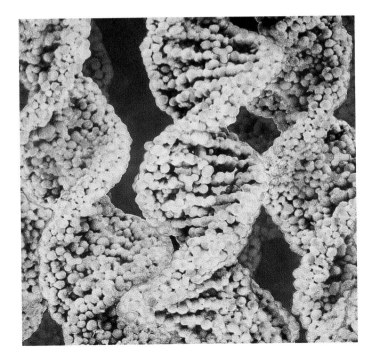

10 angstroms (1 nanometer)

10^{-9} meters

Building blocks of DNA . . .

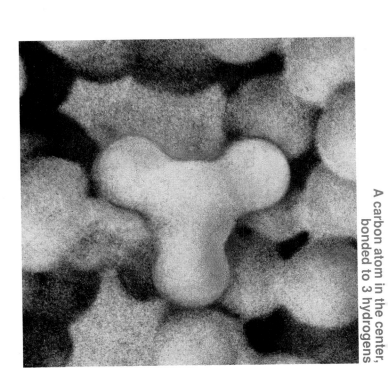

A carbon atom in the center, bonded to 3 hydrogens

1 angstrom   (100 picometers)

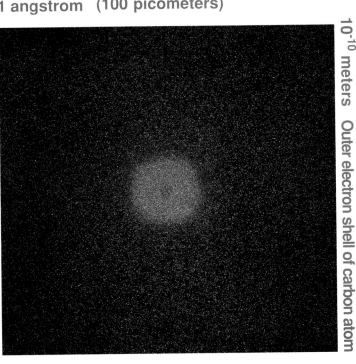

10^{-10} meters   Outer electron shell of carbon atom

Inner shell is visible in the center

10 picometers

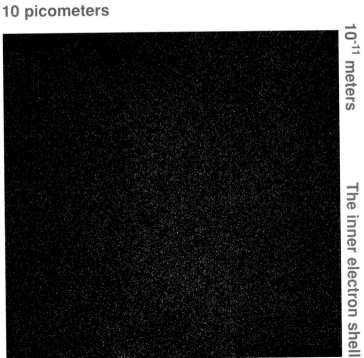

10⁻¹¹ meters

The inner electron shell

1 picometer

10^{-12} meters

Nothing

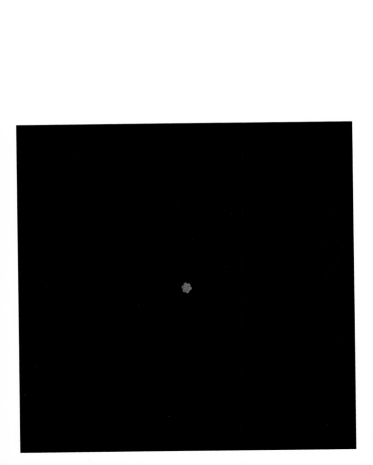

100 fermis

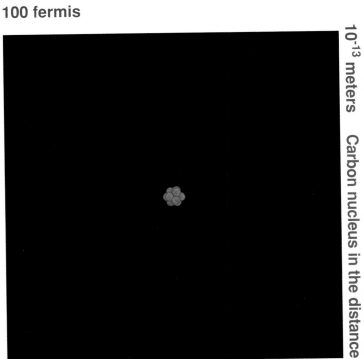

10⁻¹³ meters   Carbon nucleus in the distance

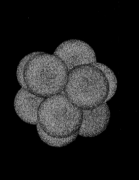

10 fermis

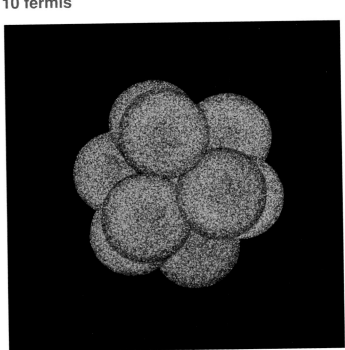

10^{-14} meters   The nucleus of a carbon atom

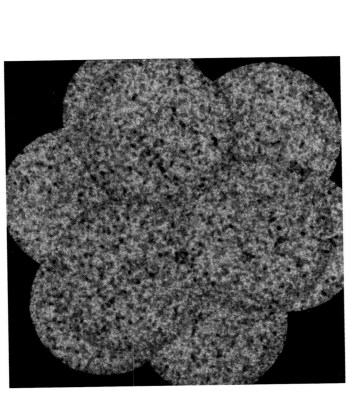